P9-CMY-399

# Philadelphia Chickens
## Deluxe Illustrated Lyrics Book

### PART ONE
## LOOK AS YOU LISTEN

Spiffy illustrations of all the songs on your Chicken Disc (CD)

### PART TWO
## SING & PLAY ALONG

All 3 billion or so words to the songs, *plus* selected music notation

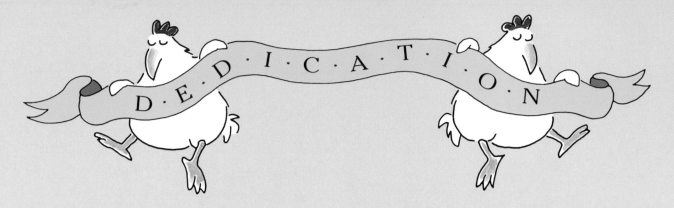

## D·E·D·I·C·A·T·I·O·N

To all of the terrific children of the entire Philly Chix cast and crew—

Caitlin, Keith, Devin, Darcy, Rachel, John, Katie,
Henry, Mamie, Grace, Louisa, Neal, Travis, Sosie,
Josh, Ruby, Katie, Théo, Nicholas, Emily, Robb,
Heather, Ben, Sedgie, Max, Quinby, Eliza,
Greta, Owen, Chelsey, Cody, Wil, Owen,
Matt, Michéal, Daniel, Christian, Spencer,
Kacie, Chris, Tommy, Lucie, Zoë, Catherine, Alice, Ned,
Katie, Elizabeth, Jack & Madeline

—and for Laura Linney, who is so charmingly persistent.

Book and Recording Copyright © and ℗ 2002 by Sandra Boynton. All rights reserved. No portion of this book or recording may be reproduced–mechanically, electronically, or by any other means, including photocopying and audio taping–without written permission of the publisher and author. Published simultaneously in Canada by Thomas Allen & Son Limited.

*Pajama Time* is based on Sandra Boynton's board book published by Workman Publishing • *Snoozers* is based on Sandra Boynton's board book published by Simon & Schuster

Library of Congress Cataloging-in-Publication Data

ON FILE

WORKMAN PUBLISHING COMPANY, INC., 225 VARICK STREET, NEW YORK, NY 10014-4381  WWW.WORKMAN.COM  WWW.SANDRABOYNTON.COM
PRINTED IN CHINA.  FIRST PRINTING: OCTOBER 2002

# LOOK AS YOU LISTEN

*A turn of the head and a swish of the tail and a tippity-tap of the toes.*
*What a glorious sight in black and white, and a touch of pink at the nose!*

# Cows

Cows.
We're remarkable COWS.
And wherever we go,
it's a fabulous show.
Oh, you know we are COWS.
~~That's right, we're COWS.~~
Such remarkable COWS.
We can sing very low.
We can dance in a row.
We are lovely and slow, oh, oh—
Yes, you know we are COWS.

If you thought that
all we could do was go moo,
then you ought to
come and see what we do.

For we are COWS.
*We're remarkable cows.*
Such remarkable COWS.
*Ooo, remarkable cows.*
And wherever we go,
*And where we go,*
it's a fabulous show.
*it's quite a show.*
Oh, you know we are
COWS,

COWS,

COWS,

COWS...

FOR MUSIC & ALL LYRICS, PLEASE TURN TO PAGE 45

*When I think of all the glorble snop I've tried so hard to explain!*
*They all look amused, or a little confused. Why can't they see what I mean?*

# SONG # 2 Nobody Understands Me

Nobody understands me,
although I wish they would.
Nobody understands me.
I hate being misunderstood.

Nobody understands me,
no matter how I try.
Nobody understands me,
and I can't understand why.

When I think of all the
glorble snop
I've tried so hard to explain!
They all look amused,
or a little confused.
Why can't they see what I mean?
(It's very snooffly.)

Nobody understands me,
though memmily blitt each day.
Nobody understands me,
but I guess zooglobble that way.

How can I make you understand?
How can I make you see?
Why does my queckery biffle you so?
Where will this ezzleboo dornut go?
What do explectionary inyews know?
When will you yuddle
for ME-E-E-E-E?

Nobody beezifies me.
Nobody febbin ud.
Kibblezy deen voo nizee!
I hate being misunderstood.

FOR MUSIC, PLEASE TURN TO PAGE 46

*If you haven't ever seen it, you can't understand—undulating chickens and a big swing band.*
*They're tight on the turns, and loose in the knees. Whatever they do, they do it with ease.*

# SONG # 3

# Philadelphia Chickens

**W**ell, I'm coming from
Connecticut on I-95,
heading toward the sunset
on the East River Drive
to the pretty little city
on the Delaware—
the Philadelphia Chickens
are sure to be there.

Oh, the Philadelphia Chickens
will be dancing tonight,
thousands of chickens
in the pale moonlight.
They can't sit still
when the trumpets play—

Strike up the band
and get out of the way.
Here come those

*Philadelphia Chickens!*
*Swing, slide, and roll.*
*Philadelphia Chickens!*
*Up, over, and stroll.*
*If you want to start*
*moving like anything,*
*find a Philadelphia Chicken*
*to teach you to swing.*

FOR MUSIC & ALL LYRICS, PLEASE TURN TO PAGE 47

*Maybe you stroll. Maybe you fly. Or maybe just float and let the river run by.*

**SONG #**
**4**

# Be Like a Duck

**I**f you want to find a rhythm
that is oh so nice,
if you want to find a rhythm,
you should take my advice.
If you want to find a rhythm,
I can show you the way:
Be like a duck.
That's what I say:
Be like a duck.
Be like a duck.
Be like a duck.

(Okay.)


A duck is so friendly.
A duck is so proud.
A duck is never ever
just a face in the crowd.
A duck is so clever.
A duck is so free.

Don't you want to be
just exactly like me?
Be like a duck.
Be like a duck.
Be like a duck.


You've got to walk the walk.
You've got to talk the talk.
And when you want to fly,
you've got to take to the sky,
and cruise......


Be like a duck.
(Yes, indeed.)
Be like a duck.
(No need for speed.)
Be like a duck.
Like a duck.
(Cool!)

FOR MUSIC & ALL LYRICS, PLEASE TURN TO PAGE 48

*Please, please, can I keep it? It followed me home. What exactly it is, I don't know.*
*Oh, please, can I keep it? It's lost and afraid. I'm sure it has nowhere to go.*

# Please, Can I Keep It?

Please, can I keep it?
It followed me home.
It seems to be sad and alone.
Oh, please, can I keep it?
It's friendly and shy,
and I don't have
a pet of my own.

Please, please, can I keep it?
It followed me home.
What exactly it is, I don't know.
Oh, please, can I keep it?
It's lost and afraid.
And I'm sure it has
nowhere to go.

I could find it a bowl
and give it some food
whenever it needs to be fed.
Or I maybe won't have to.
It seems very smart.
See?
It's helping itself
to our bread!
*Really* helping itself
to our bread.
And some fruit.
**ALL** the fruit.
Now the juice.
And the flowers.
And the vase.  (Wow!)

FOR MUSIC & ALL LYRICS, PLEASE TURN TO PAGE 49

*OOO, Snuggle Puppy of mine! Everything about you is especially fine.*

SONG # 6

# Snuggle Puppy

**W**ell, I have a thing to tell you,
and it won't take long:
The way I feel about you
is a kind of a song.
It starts with an *OOO*,
and ends with a kiss,
and all along the middle,
it goes something like this—

It goes:
*OOO, Snuggle Puppy of mine!*
*Everything about you*
*is especially fine.*
*I love what you are.*
*I love what you do.*
*Fuzzy little Snuggle Puppy,*
*I love you.*

I say,
*OOO, Snuggle Puppy of mine!*
*Everything about you*
*is especially fine.*
*I love what you are.*
*I love what you do.*
*OOOOO! I love you.* [KISS!]

Well, I wanted just to tell you,
and it didn't take long:
The way I feel about you
is a kind of a song.
I started with *OOO*,
I gave you a kiss.
I hope you liked the middle.
Now we'll end like this:

**[BIG SMOOCH!]**

FOR MUSIC, PLEASE TURN TO PAGE 50

*I like to gripe. I like to whine. And I refuse to share whatever is mine. I won't share.*

# I Like to Fuss

*Mostly I am pleasant. Mostly I am good.*
*I answer you politely, just as you say I should.*
*Yes, mostly I am perfect. You don't hear me complain.*
*But after so much sunshine, we need a little rain:*

I like to fuss.
I like to moan.
I like to stand on my chair
and say,

## "Leave me alone!"

Don't bother me.


I like to grump.
I like to brood.
I like to stomp
all around
in a truly terrible mood.

When everybody, more or less,
tells me to stop, I go.
When everybody says
the answer is yes,
I find myself saying,

## "No, no, no!"


I like to gripe.
I like to whine.
And I refuse to share
whatever is mine.
I WON'T SHARE.

FOR MUSIC
& ALL LYRICS,
PLEASE TURN
TO PAGE 51

*It can be amusing to see us snoozing—snoozing wherever we go.*

# Snoozers

We like to snooze
in the morning.
We like to snooze all day.
We like to snooze
whenever we choose—
Snoozing our cares away.

We like to snooze
in the summer.
We like to snooze in the spring.
With the wintertime blues,
we snooze and snooze—
Snoozing like anything.

Snooze in the sun.
Snooze in the rain.
Snooze in the fog and snow.

It can be amusing
to see us snoozing,
snoozing wherever we go.

We like to snooze horizontal.
We like to snooze upside-down.
We like to snooze
however we choose—
Snoozing around the town.

But when the world grows quiet
and the evening moon is bright,
we put on pajamas
and hug all our mommas,
and never fall asleep
all night, all night.
We never fall asleep all night.

We're singing.......................

HANG ON TO
YOUR HAT...

*We're not snoozy, Momma! Wake up, Momma, now!*
*We slept all day and now we want to play, so come and let us show you how!*

# Snoozers (Part Two)

WE'RE NOT SNOOZY, MOMMA!
WAKE UP, MOMMA, NOW!
WE SLEPT ALL DAY
AND NOW WE WANT TO PLAY,
SO COME AND LET US
SHOW YOU HOW!

WE'RE NOT SNOOZY, MOMMA!
WAKE UP, MOMMA, PLEASE!
WE KNOW WHO'S
GOT THE SNOOZER BLUES,
'CAUSE WE DON'T WANT
THOSE DORMEZ-VOUS!

ARE YOU SLEEPING,
BROTHER?
WAKE UP, BROTHER JOHN!
THE MIDNIGHT BELL

SAYS ALL IS WELL.
KEEP RINGING
THAT BELL TILL
DAWN, DAWN, DAWN.
DANG-DINGING IT
ALL NIGHT LONG.
WE'RE SINGING IT
ALL NIGHT LONG.
GONNA
ROCK ROCK ROCK
AROUND
HALF THE CLOCK,
KEEP PLAYING IT
ALL NIGHT LONG.

*No snoozing!*
*We're cruising!*

FOR MUSIC
& ALL LYRICS,
PLEASE TURN
TO PAGE 52

*I have loved you before, I could love you some more, and I long to be with you again.*

SONG # 9

# Faraway Cookies

When the sunlight has gone
and the green hills turn gray
and the day turns to evening
somehow,
then I'm thinking of you,
though you're so far away,
and I'm wanting you
close to me now.

*Oh, Chocolate Chip Cookies*
*so high on the shelf,*
*hiding inside of the jar—*
*I'm not tall enough*
*to reach you myself.*
*So near, and yet so very far.*

I can never forget you.
You're all I adore.
Through many long moments
I've tried.

I call out your name,
but I'll have to do more
to bring you back here
to my side.

*Oh, Chocolate Chip Cookies*
*so high on the shelf,*
*hiding inside of the jar—*
*I'm not tall enough*
*to reach you myself.*
*So near, and yet so very far.*

If I had three wishes,
they'd all be for you.
If I had my way,
you'd be mine.
Oh, the reach wouldn't matter
if I had a ladder.
If I weren't so short,
we'd be fine.

FOR MUSIC & ALL LYRICS, PLEASE TURN TO PAGE 54

SONG #
10

# The Interm

**O**h, we've come to intermission
so it's time to stretch your toes.
And if you are an
AARDVARK,
you should also stretch your nose.

When you hear
the bell go
**"BING-BONG!,"**
intermission
has begun,
and when you hear
another
**"BING-BONG!,"**
then
intermission's done.

# ission Song!

Oh, we've come to intermission
so it's time to stretch your toes.
*(Each and every little toe.)*
And if you're still an
AARDVARK,
you should also stretch your nose.
*(Your nifty nose.)*

We hope you like our singing.
We hope you like the show.
We hope you like...spaghetti.
[BING-BONG!]
It's time for us to go.
. . . . . . . . . . . . . . . . .
[BING-BONG!]

Now intermission's over.
It wasn't very long.
Please hurry to your places
to enjoy another song.

FOR MUSIC
& ALL LYRICS,
PLEASE TURN
TO PAGE 55

TOP ROW: *Bob, Bob, Bob and Bob, Bob, Bob, Bob*
BOTTOM ROW: *Bob, Bob, Bob, Bob, and Bob, Bob, Bob, Simon James Alexander Ragsdale III*

# Fifteen Animals

I really like animals,
I like them a lot.
Fifteen animals is what I've got.
I've got fifteen animals—
they're friendly and tame—
and I've given each one
a special name:

I've got a cat named Bob,
and a dog named Bob,
and two fish called
Bob and Bob.
Then there's Bob, my hamster,
and Bob, my horse,
and my piglet, known as
Bob, of course.

Yeah, I really like animals,
I like them a lot.
Fifteen animals is what I've got.
I've got fifteen animals—
they're friendly and tame—
and I've given each one
a special name:

Well, there's my rabbit, Bob,
and his bunny wife, Bob,
and their kids, Bob, Bob, and Bob.
There's Bob the mouse,
and Bob the bird,
and my turtle,
*Simon James Alexander Ragsdale III.*

FOR MUSIC, PLEASE TURN TO PAGE 56

*A tummy without you just wouldn't be right. Little Belly Button, you're a beautiful sight.*

**SONG # 12**

# Belly Button (Round)

*So round. So profound. So great to contemplate…*

Belly Belly Button,
you're oh so fine.
OOO, Belly Button,
I'm so happy you're mine.
A tummy without you
just wouldn't be right.
Little Belly Button,
you're a beautiful sight.
Belly! Belly button!

(*Yeah.*)

Patty pat pat.
Baby fat.
Patty pat pat, baby fat.
Itty bitty button in the middle of that.

FOR MUSIC, PLEASE TURN TO PAGE 57

*We have to hurry far away and then we hurry near*
*and we have to hurry everywhere and be both there and here...*

SONG #
13

# BusyBusyBusy

**WE'RE**

*very very busy
and we've got a lot to do
and we haven't got a minute
to explain it all to you
for on SundayMondayTuesday
there are people we must see
and on WednesdayThursdayFriday
we're as busy as can be
with our most important meetings
and our most important calls
and we have to do so many things
and post them on the walls.*

**THEN**

*we have to hurry to the south
and then we hurry north
and we're talking every minute
as we hurry back and forth
and we have to hurry to the east
and then we hurry west
and we're talking every minute
and we don't have time to rest
and we have to do it faster
or it never will be done
and we have no time for listening
or anything that's fun.*

FOR MUSIC & ALL LYRICS, PLEASE TURN TO PAGE 58

*Now, no one expects a Tyrannosaurus Rex to be friendly, and silly, and shy.*
*But if you knew me, you'd find that I'm gentle and kind. Yes, I'm really a sensitive guy.*

SONG # 14

# Those Dinosaur Blues

*I'm a dino with a low, low voice. It's not my fault. I had no choice.*
*Everyone's afraid of me. I'm very nice. Why don't they see?*

I've got those dinosaur blues
from my hat to my shoes.
I'm so terribly blue.
Oh, woe, what can I do?
I've got those dinosaur blues.

I've got those dinosaur blues.
Got no hat.
Don't have shoes.
But I know if I had,
I would still feel so bad.
Oh, those dinosaur blues.

Oh why, oh why
am I the scariest guy?
I am longing to play,
but you all run away
without saying goodbye.
And I just want to cry.

I've got those dinosaur blues.
How I wish I could choose
that you would love me a lot
since I'm cute. But I'm not.
I've got those dinosaur blues.

FOR MUSIC & ALL LYRICS, PLEASE TURN TO PAGE 59

# Dinosaur, Dinosaur &
# Jump Rope Jive

**KIDS:** *DINOSAUR, DINOSAUR, LONELY AND SHY.*
*DINOSAUR, DINOSAUR, READY TO CRY.*
*TYRANNOSAUR, BANANASAUR, O, SAURUS OF MINE,*
*YOU'VE GOT A LOT OF BUDDIES*
*AND YOU'RE GONNA BE FINE—YOU'VE GOT 1, 2, 3, 4 …*

**DINOSAUR:** Get over that rope and count some more.

**KIDS:** Yeah!

(*SUDDENLY, FROM OUT OF NOWHERE, APPEAR …*)
**THE AMAZING SINGING CHICKENS:**

Dinosaur, Dinosaur, so lonely and shy.
Dinosaur, Dinosaur, ready to cry.
Tyrannosaur, Bananasaur, O, saurus of mine!
You've got a lot of buddies
and you're gonna be fine.
You've got **1** and **2** and **3** and **4**.
Get over that rope and count some more.
You've got to skip in time.
You've got to move your feet.
You've got to keep on counting
to that jump rope beat.

FOR MUSIC & ALL LYRICS, PLEASE TURN TO PAGE 60

*The only way to get there is by Piggy Express—You've got to close your eyes, and then whisper, "Ooo, YES!"*
*A tiny little piggy with silver wings touches your hand, and softly sings: "Pig Island! Pig Island!"*

# Pig Island

There is one perfect place in the whole wide world
where noses are crinkled and tails are curled,
where squeals are happy and smiles are bright,
and the wind is gentle all day and night:

Pig Island! Pig Island! What a beautiful place to be.
They play on the beaches the color of peaches
there by the turquoise sea, oh my, under a blue, blue sky.

FOR MUSIC
& ALL LYRICS,
PLEASE TURN
TO PAGE 61

*Pajammy to the left. Pajammy to the right. Everybody's wearing them on Saturday night.*

# Pajama Time

The moon is up.
It's getting late.
Let's get ready to celebrate—
It's Pajama Time!
Oh, it's Pajama Time!
Pull on the bottoms,
put on the top.
Get yourself set
to pajama-dee-bop—
It's Pajama Time!
Yeah, it's Pajama Time!

Some are old and some are new.
Some are red and some are blue.
Some are fuzzy. Some are not.
But we can all pajammy
in whatever we've got.
It's Pajama Time!
Hey yeah, it's Pajama Time!

Pajammy to the left.
Pajammy to the right.
Everybody's wearing them
on Saturday night.
Now all around the room
in one big line,
wearing our pajamas
and looking so fine!

*Ooooooooo……*
Some are pink
and some are green.
Some are the ugliest
you've ever seen.
They might be stripey
or polka dot,
but we can all pajammy
in whatever we've got.
It's Pajama Time!

FOR MUSIC & ALL LYRICS, PLEASE TURN TO PAGE 62

♪ *"The chickens in the bathtub…"* ♪

# Silly Lullaby

Go to sleep, my zoodle,
my fibblety-fitsy foo.
Go to sleep, sweet noodle.
It's time to say, "Ah-choo."

The chickens in the bathtub,
the closet full of sheep,
the sneakers in the freezer
are all drifting off to sleep.

Go to sleep, my zoodle,
my fibblety-fitsy foo.
Go to sleep, sweet noodle.
The owl is whispering, "Moo."

FOR MUSIC, PLEASE TURN TO PAGE 63

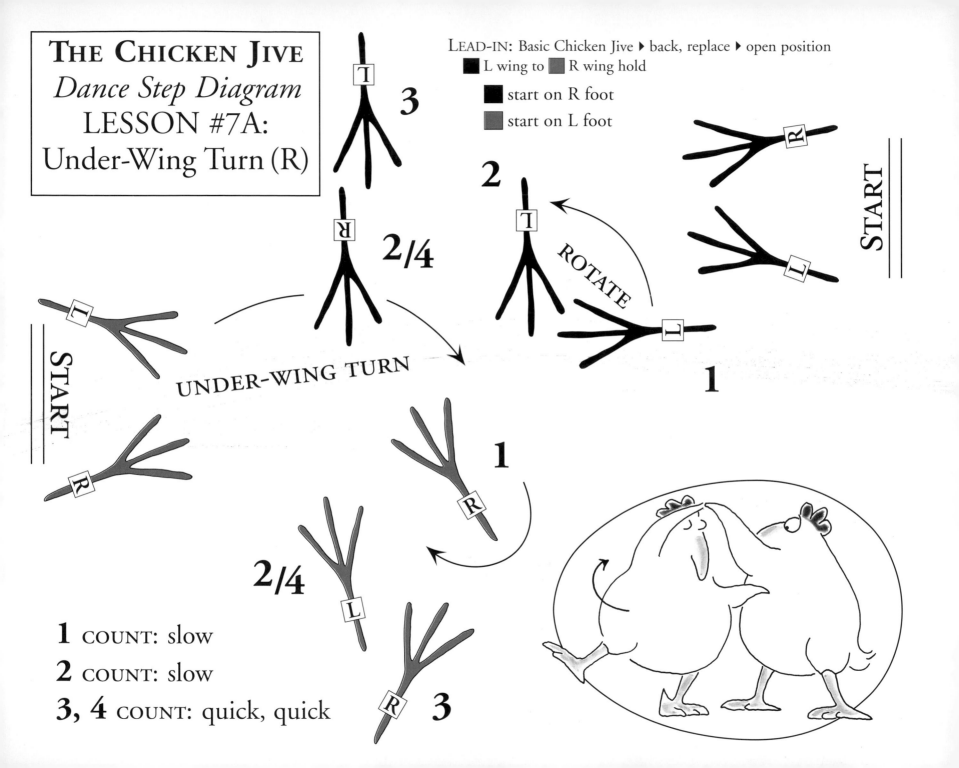

# THE CHICKEN JIVE
*Dance Step Diagram*
LESSON #7A:
Under-Wing Turn (R)

LEAD-IN: Basic Chicken Jive ▶ back, replace ▶ open position
■ L wing to ■ R wing hold
■ start on R foot
■ start on L foot

3

2/4

2

ROTATE

START

START

UNDER-WING TURN

1

1

2/4

3

**1** COUNT: slow
**2** COUNT: slow
**3, 4** COUNT: quick, quick

# SING & PLAY ALONG

# Cows

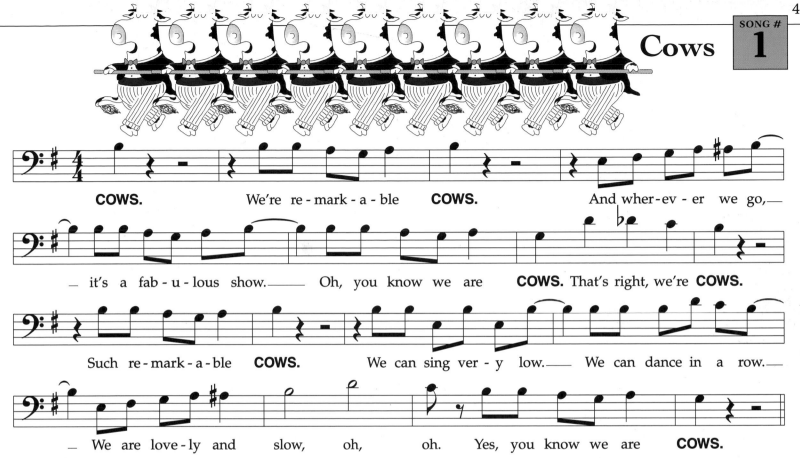

COWS. We're re-mark-a-ble COWS. And wher-ev-er we go,—

— it's a fab-u-lous show.—— Oh, you know we are COWS. That's right, we're COWS.

Such re-mark-a-ble COWS. We can sing ver-y low.—— We can dance in a row.——

— We are love-ly and slow, oh, oh. Yes, you know we are COWS.

If you thought that
all we could do was go moo,
then you ought to
come and see what we do.
For we are
COWS.
    *We're remarkable cows.*
Such remarkable COWS.
    *Ooo, remarkable cows.*
And wherever we go,
    *And where we go,*
it's a fabulous show.
    *it's quite a show.*
Oh, you know we are
COWS, COWS, COWS, COWS...

A turn of the head
and a swish of the tail
and a tippity tap of the toes.
What a glorious sight
in black and white
and a touch of pink
at the nose!
Here we go again: COWS.
    *Okay, we're cows.*
We're remarkable COWS.
    *Say hay, we're cows.*
We can sing very low.
We can dance in a row.
We are lovely and slow, oh, oh—
Oh, you know we are COWS.

If you thought that
all we could do was go moo,
then you ought to
know that before us,
there's not been a chorus
line so fine!
'Cause we are
COWS.
    *How now, we're cows.*
We're remarkable COWS.
    *Now we're taking our bows.*
And wherever we go,
it's a fabulous show.
Oh, you know we are COWS.
And wherever we go,

*And where we go,*
*it's quite a show.*
    *it's quite a show.*
Oh, you know we are COWS!
    *So very fine.*
In a row, we are COWS!
    *A chorus line.*
We're incredible COWS!
    *Oh, yes, indeed.*
Unforgettable COWS!
    *An unusual breed.*
Pay attention, we're COWS!
**DID WE MENTION WE'RE
COWS?** *(Buh bumm bumm...)*
Now our number is through.
Mooby dooby moo moo.

SONG #
**2**

# Nobody Understands Me

No - bod - y— un-der-stands me,— al-though I wish they would. No - bod - y— un-der-stands me.   I

hate be - ing mis-un-der - stood.     No - bod - y— un-der - stands me,— no mat-ter how I

try.   No - bod-y— un-der-stands me,   and   I can't un-der-stand— why.—    When I

think of all———— the— glor-ble snop      I've tried so hard— to ex -

plain!————     They all look a - mused,     or a lit - tle con - fused.

Why— can't they see——— what I mean? (It's ver - y snooff-ly.)

| | | |
|---|---|---|
| Nobody understands me, | How can I make you understand? | When will you yuddle for me? |
| Though memmily blitt each day. | How can I make you see? | Nobody beezifies me— |
| Nobody understands me, | Why does my queckery biffle you so? | Nobody febbin ud. |
| But I guess | Where will this ezzleboo dornut go? | KIBBLEZY DEEN VOO NIZEE! |
| zooglobble that way. | What do explectionary inyews know? | I hate being misunderstood. |

# Philadelphia Chickens

Well, I'm coming from
Connecticut on I-95,
heading toward the sunset
on the East River Drive
to the pretty little city
on the Delaware—
the Philadelphia Chickens
are sure to be there.
Oh, the Philadelphia Chickens
will be dancing tonight,
thousands of chickens
in the pale moonlight.
They can't sit still
when the trumpets play—
Strike up the band
and get out of the way.
Here come those

**[SEE REFRAIN BELOW]**

If you haven't ever seen it,
you can't understand—
Undulating chickens
and a big swing band.
They're tight on the turns,
and loose in the knees.
Whatever they do,

they do it with ease.
Yo, the Philadelphia Chickens
will be dancing tonight,
thousands of chickens
in the pale moonlight.
There's nothing like a chicken
that knows how to swing.
Poultry in motion is a
beautiful thing. Just watch those

Philadelphia Chickens!
Swing, slide, and roll.
Philadelphia Chickens!
Up, over, and stroll.
Philadelphia Chickens!
Move those chicken feet.
Philadelphia Chickens!
Feel. That. Chicken beat.
If you want to start
moving like anything,
find a Philadelphia Chicken
to teach you to swing.

*(Now swing it, Chickens!)*
Hey, hey. Oh, no.
Let it swing, and watch 'em go.
You've got to like

what a chicken has—
A little bit of attitude,
a whole lot of jazz!
Now the feathers are flying
and the music is great.
The chickens keep flocking
right over the gate.
Lancaster County's
in a state of alarm—
How're they gonna keep them
down on the farm?
How're they gonna keep them
down on the farm?
*They're never gonna keep them
down on the farm, once they've been*

Philadelphia Chickens!
Swing, slide, and roll.
Philadelphia Chickens!
Up, over, and stroll.
Ho! Philadelphia Chickens!
    *Philadelphia Chickens!*
Move those chicken feet.
    *Move those chicken feet.*
Philadelphia Chickens!
    *Philadelphia Chickens!*

Feel. That. Chicken beat.
If you want to start
moving like anything,
find a Philadelphia Chicken
to teach you to swing.

Oh, the Philadelphia Chickens
will be dancing tonight,
thousands of chickens
in the pale moonlight.
I don't know much,
but I know one thing:
these are serious chickens
when it comes to swing.
So unique. Beak to beak.
Strutting their stuff.
Can't get enough of that
Hot. Cool. Ecstatical thing.
Oooooo,
those chickens of swing.
    Jazz, jive, and chickens
    and the moon above
    Right here in the city
    of chickenly love.
**CHICKENS!**
    *(Oh my.)*

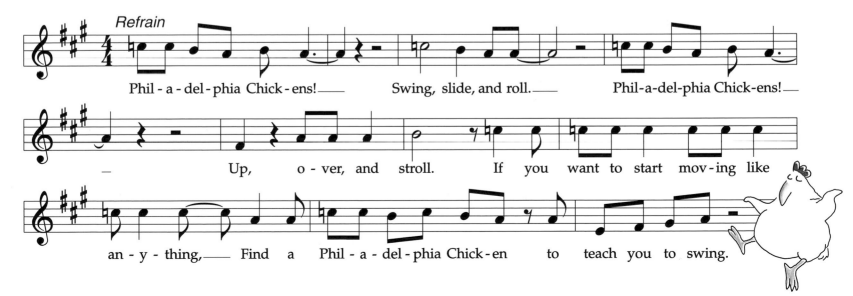

*Refrain*

Phil - a - del - phia Chick - ens!____ Swing, slide, and roll.____ Phil - a - del - phia Chick - ens!____

___ Up, o - ver, and stroll. If you want to start mov - ing like

an - y - thing,____ Find a Phil - a - del - phia Chick - en to teach you to swing.

SONG # **4**

# Be Like a Duck

No no. That's not the way to go.
You've got to go......................slow.

If you want to find a rhy-thm that is oh so nice, If you want to find a rhy-thm, you should take my ad-vice. If you want to find a rhy-thm, I can show you the way: Be like a duck. That's what I say: Be like a duck. Be like a duck. Be like a duck. (O-kay.)

A duck is so friendly.
A duck is so proud.
A duck is never ever
just a face in the crowd.
A duck is so clever.
A duck is so free.
Don't you want to be
just exactly like me?
Be like a duck.
Be like a duck.
Be like a duck.
  You've got to walk the walk.
  You've got to talk the talk.
  And when you want to fly,
  you've got to take to the sky,
  and cruise......

Be like a duck.
*Yes, indeed.*
Be like a duck.
*No need for speed.*
Be like a duck.
Like a duck. *Cool!*
  Maybe you stroll.
  Maybe you fly.
  Or maybe just float
  and let the river run by.
  When the rain starts falling,
  let it roll off your back.
  Open up your beak and go
  QUACK-QUACK QUACK—
Be like a duck.
  *You don't have to fret.*

Be like a duck.
  *You can just get wet.*
Be like a duck.
Be like a duck.
Be like a duck. *Get down.*
  You've got to walk the walk.
  You've got to talk the talk.
  And when you want to fly,
  you've got to take to the sky,
  and cruise......
Maybe you stroll.
Maybe you fly.
Or maybe just float
and let the river run by.
When the rain starts falling,
let it roll off your back.

Open up your beak and go
QUACK-QUACK QUACK—
Be like a duck.
  *You don't have to fuss.*
Be like a duck.
  *You could be like us.*
Be like a duck.
Be like a duck.
Be like a duck.
  You've got to walk the walk.
  You've got to talk the talk.
  And when you want to fly,
  you've got to take to the sky,
  and cruuuuuuuuuuise.........
*Gone!*
Like a duck.

# Please, Can I Keep It?

HEY, MOM! *Come into the kitchen and close your eyes. I've brought you home a big surprise...*
*Isn't it* ADORABLE? *Okay, Boy, now SIT. SIT. SIT. Never mind.*

Please, can I keep it?   It   fol-lowed me home.— It   seems to be sad— and a-lone.—   Oh,

please, can  I  keep it?   It's friend-ly and shy,—  And  I  don't have a pet of my own.—  Please,

please, can I keep it?   It   fol-lowed me home.— What ex-act-ly it is,—  I don't know.—  Oh,

please, can I keep it?   It's lost  and  a-fraid,—  And I'm sure it has no-where  to   go.

I could find it a bowl
and give it some food
whenever it needs to be fed.
Or I maybe won't have to.
It seems very smart.
See? It's helping itself
to our bread!
*Really* helping itself
to our bread.
And some fruit.

**ALL** the fruit.
Now the juice.
And the flowers.
And the vase. (Wow!)
Please, can I keep it?
Its fur is so soft,
though I know it is
shedding a lot.
It can sleep on my floor,
if it fits through the door.

It could sleep in
the hallway if not.
Oh, please, please,
*please* can I keep it?
It's thumping its tail.
It has such a lovable whine.
Please, can I keep it?
Just look at those eyes.
I think it would
love to be mine.

I *know* it would
love to be mine.
And yours.
Say yes.
Oh, please.
Oh, please.
Oh, please.
Oh, please.

{"Oh, *please?*"}

SONG #
**6**

# Snuggle Puppy

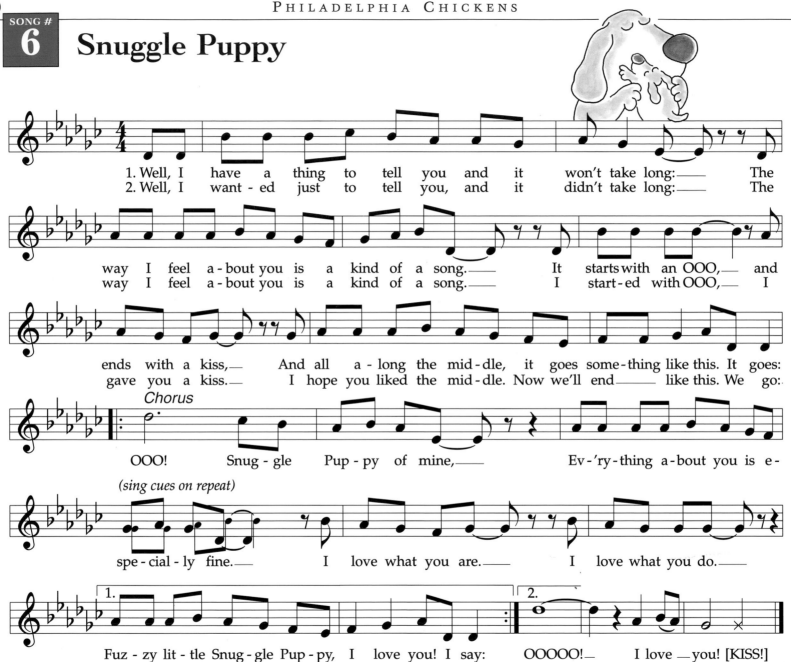

1. Well, I have a thing to tell you and it won't take long:____ The
2. Well, I want-ed just to tell you, and it didn't take long:____ The

way I feel a-bout you is a kind of a song.____ It starts with an OOO,____ and
way I feel a-bout you is a kind of a song.____ I start-ed with OOO,____ I

ends with a kiss,____ And all a-long the mid-dle, it goes some-thing like this. It goes:
gave you a kiss.____ I hope you liked the mid-dle. Now we'll end____ like this. We go:

*Chorus*

OOO! Snug - gle Pup - py of mine,____ Ev-'ry-thing a-bout you is e-

*(sing cues on repeat)*

spe - cial - ly fine.____ I love what you are.____ I love what you do.____

1.
Fuz - zy lit - tle Snug - gle Pup - py, I love you! I say:

2.
OOOOO!____ I love ____you! [KISS!]

# I Like to Fuss

*Mostly I am pleasant. Mostly I am good.*
*I answer you politely, just as you say I should.*
*Yes, mostly I am perfect. You don't hear me complain.*
*But after so much sunshine, we need a little rain:*

I like to fuss. I like to moan. I like to stand on my chair and say,

"LEAVE ME A-LONE"!— Don't both-er me. I like to grump. I like to

brood. I like to stomp all a-round— in a tru-ly ter-ri-ble mood.—

BAD, BAD MOOD. (Yeah.)
*BAD, BAD MOOD, oo oo.*
When everybody,
more or less,
tells me to stop, I go. *SHE GOES.*
When everybody says
the answer is yes,
I find myself saying,
no, no, no!
I like to gripe. *WHOA, OH.*
I like to whine. *DOO-WAHH!*
And I refuse to share
whatever is mine.
I won't share.

*SHE WON'T SHARE IT.*
*SHE WON'T SHARE.*
*SHE WON'T BE NICE.*
Not nice.
*SHE WON'T BE FAIR.*
Not fair.
And if you don't like it,
I say I don't care. I DON'T CARE.

*WHO CARES?*
*WHO CARES?*
*WHO CARES?*
If you say STOP,
then I say GO.
If you say YES,

then I say NO-oh-oh.
I just want to get
one thing straight:
If you're in a hurry,
I say, IF you're in a hurry,
if you're **R E A L L Y**
in a hurry, I'll make you wait.
*COME ON.*
No.
*IT'S LATE.*
**No.**
*LET'S GO.*
**No!**

I like to yell. *SHE LIKES TO YELL.*
I like to snit. *SHE'LL EVEN SNIT.*
I like to holler and throw
a fabulous fit:
**NO. NO. NO. NO. NO.**
**NO!!!!!!** (Sigh.)
But in a while,
when I am through,
it's possible I'll sing
a nicer song for you...
*OH, WON'T YOU PLEASE?*
Nah. I don't want to.
*Awwww.*

**SONG #**
**8** **Snoozers**

We like to snooze in the morn - ing. We like to snooze all day.

We like to snooze when - ev - er we choose,— Snooz-ing our cares a - way.

We like to snooze in the sum - mer. We like to snooze in the spring.— With the

win - ter - time blues, we snooze and snooze,— Snooz-ing like an - y - thing.—

Snooze in the sun.
Snooze in the rain.
Snooze in the fog and snow.
It can be amusing to see us snoozing,
snoozing wherever we go.

We like to snooze horizontal.
We like to snooze upside-down.
We like to snooze
however we choose—
Snoozing around the town.

But when the world grows quiet
and the evening moon is bright,
we put on pajamas
and hug all our mommas,
and never fall asleep all night,

all night.
We never
fall asleep
all night.
*We're singing*...............

# Snoozers (Part Two)

WE'RE NOT SNOO-ZY, MOM - MA! WAKE UP, MOM - MA, NOW!___ WE

SLEPT ALL DAY___ AND NOW___ WE WANT TO PLAY,___ SO COME AND LET US SHOW YOU HOW!_

___ WE'RE NOT SNOO - ZY, MOM - MA! WAKE UP, MOM - MA, PLEASE!_

WE KNOW WHO'S_ GOT THE SNOO-ZER BLUES,_ 'CAUSE WE DON'T WANT THOSE DOR - MEZ - VOUS!

| | | | |
|---|---|---|---|
| ARE YOU SLEEPING, BROTHER? | AROUND HALF THE CLOCK, | WE'RE SINGING IT | ALL NIGHT LONG. |
| WAKE UP, BROTHER JOHN! | KEEP PLAYING IT | ALL NIGHT LONG. | *No snoozing! We're cruising!* |
| THE MIDNIGHT BELL | ALL NIGHT LONG. *We said,* | WE SLEPT ALL DAY AND | PLAYING IT |
| SAYS ALL IS WELL. | ARE YOU SLEEPING, BROTHER? | NOW WE WANT TO PLAY, | ALL NIGHT LONG. |
| KEEP RINGING THAT BELL | WAKE UP, BROTHER JOHN! | KEEP PLAYING IT | KEEP PLAYING IT |
| TILL DAWN, DAWN, DAWN. | THE MIDNIGHT BELL | ALL NIGHT LONG. | ALL NIGHT LONG. |
| DANG-DINGING IT | SAYS ALL IS WELL. | KEEP PLAYING IT | KEEP PLAYING IT |
| ALL NIGHT LONG. | KEEP RINGING THAT BELL | ALL NIGHT LONG. | ALL NIGHT LONG. |
| WE'RE SINGING IT | TILL DAWN, DAWN, DAWN. | WE'RE PLAYING IT | KEEP PLAYING IT ALL NI... |
| ALL NIGHT LONG. | DANG-DINGING IT | ALL NIGHT LONG. | *Oh, hi, Mom!* |
| GONNA ROCK ROCK ROCK | ALL NIGHT LONG. | KEEP PLAYING IT | *Hey, Mom.* |

### SONG # 9 Faraway Cookies

When the sun-light has gone and the green hills turn gray And the day turns to eve-ning some-how,— Then I'm think-ing of you,— though you're so far a-way,— And I'm want-ing you close to me

*Chorus*

now.— Oh, Choc-olate Chip Cook-ies so high on the shelf, Hid-ing in-side of the jar,— I'm not tall e-nough— to reach you my-self. So near, and yet so ve-ry far.—

I can never forget you.
You're all I adore.
Through many long
moments I've tried.
I call out your name,
but I'll have to do more
to bring you back here
to my side.
*Oh, Chocolate Chip Cookies*
*so high on the shelf,*
*hiding inside of the jar—*

*I'm not tall enough*
*to reach you myself.*
*So near, and yet so very far.*
If I had three wishes,
they'd all be for you.
If I had my way,
you'd be mine.
Oh, the reach
wouldn't matter
if I had a ladder.
If I weren't so short,

we'd be fine.
I believe we will be
back together some day.
I cannot be happy till then.
I have loved you before,
I could love you some more,
and I long to be
with you again.
When the sunlight
has gone and the green hills
turn gray...

*Oh, Chocolate Chip Cookies*
*so high on the shelf,*
*hiding inside of the jar—*
*I'm not tall enough*
*to reach you myself.*
*So near, and yet*
*so very far.*
And I wish
I could be
where
you are.

# The Intermission Song!

Oh, we've come to in-ter-mis-sion so it's time to stretch your toes. And if you are an aard-vark, you should

al - so stretch your nose. When you hear the bell go "BING BONG!," in - ter -

mis - sion has be-gun, And when you hear an-oth - er "BING BONG!," then in-ter-mis-sion's done.

Oh, we've come to intermission so it's time to stretch your toes. *(Each and every little toe.)*
And if you're still an AARDVARK, you should also stretch your nose. *(Your nifty nose.)*
We hope you like our singing. We hope you like the show. We hope you like...spaghetti.
*WE SOUND GREAT!*
Spaaa-ghettiiiiiiiiiiii**[BING-BONG!]**iiiii...*Ahhhh!*...iiiiii**iiiiiiiii[BING-BONG! BING-BONG!]**iiiiiiii **[CLANG!]** *Uh-oh*
It's time for us to go.

**[BING-BONG!]**
Now intermission's over.
It wasn't very long.
Please hurry to your places
to enjoy another song.

*(Thank you.)*

# Fifteen Animals

I real-ly like an-i-mals. I like them a lot.—— Fif-teen an-i-mals is

what I've got.—— I've got fif-teen an-i-mals, they're friend-ly and tame,—— And I've

giv-en each one a spe-cial name:—— I've got a cat named Bob, and a

dog named Bob,—— and two fish called Bob and Bob.—— Then there's Bob, my ham - ster, and

Bob, my horse, and my pig-let known as Bob, of course.

Yeah, I really like animals,
I like them a lot.
Fifteen animals is what I've got.
I've got fifteen animals—
they're friendly and tame—

and I've given each one
a special name:
Well, there's my rabbit, Bob,
and his bunny wife, Bob,
and their kids, Bob, Bob, and Bob.

There's Bob the mouse,
and Bob the bird,
and my turtle,
*Simon James Alexander Ragsdale III.*
*(Here, Bob!)*

# Belly Button (Round)

(Belly... Button. ROUND. ROUND. ROUND.)

*So round. So profound. So great to contemplate...*

Bel-ly Bel-ly But-ton, you're oh— so fine.— OOO, Bel-ly But-ton, I'm so

hap-py you're mine.— A tum-my with-out— you just would-n't be right.—

Lit-tle Bel-ly But-ton, you're a beau-ti-ful sight.— Bel-ly!— Bel-ly But-ton! (Yeah.)

*Patty pat pat.*
(Patty pat pat.)
*Baby fat.*
(Baby fat.)
*Patty pat pat, baby fat.*
*Itty bitty button in the middle of that.*

**SONG # 13**

# BusyBusyBusy

We're ver-y ver-y bus-y and we've got a lot to do and we have-n't got a min-ute to ex-plain it all to you for on Sun-dayMon-dayTues-day there are peo-ple we must see and on Wednes-dayThurs-dayFri-day we're as bus-y as can be with our most im-por-tant meet-ings and our most im-por-tant calls and we have to do so man-y things and post them on the walls.

*With our most important meetings*
*and our most important calls*
*and we have to do so many things*
*and post them on the walls.*

### THEN

we have to hurry to the south
and then we hurry north
and we're talking every minute
as we hurry back and forth
and we have to hurry to the east
and then we hurry west
and we're talking every minute
and we don't have time to rest
and we have to do it faster
or it never will be done
and we have no time for listening
or anything that's fun.

*Oh, we have to do it faster*
*or it never will be done*
*and we have no*
*time for listening*
*or anything that's fun.*

### FOR

we're very very busy
and we've got a lot to do
and we haven't got a minute
to explain it all to you
for on SundayMondayTuesday
there are people we must see
and on WednesdayThursdayFriday
we're as busy as can be
with our most important meetings
and our most important calls
and we have to do so many things
and post them on the walls.

*With our most important meetings*
*and our most important calls*
*and we have to do so many things*
*and post them on the walls.*

### AND *("Next.")*

we have to hurry to the left,
and then we hurry right *("Next.")*
and we're talking every minute
as we hurry day and night *("Next.")*

and we have to have our lunches
though we don't have time to chew
*("Next.")* and we have to order
many things in gray and navy blue
but we think supplies are limited
    (restrictions may apply)
so we'll call the operators
who are surely standing by:

"WE'RE VERY VERY BUSY
AND WE'VE GOT A LOT TO DO
AND WE HAVEN'T GOT A MINUTE
TO EXPLAIN IT ALL TO YOU
FOR ON SUNDAYMONDAYTUESDAY
THERE ARE PEOPLE WE MUST SEE
AND ON WEDNESDAYTHURSDAYFRIDAY
WE'RE AS BUSY AS CAN BE..."

with our most important meetings
and our most important calls
and we have to do so many things
and post them on the walls.

*With our most important meetings*
*and our most important calls*

*and we have to do so many things*
*and post them on the walls.*

### NOW

we have to hurry far away
and then we hurry near
and we have to hurry everywhere
and be both there and here
and we have to send out messages
by e-mail, phone, and fax
and we're talking every minute
and we really can't relax
and we think there is a reason
to be running neck-and-neck
and it must be quite important
but we don't have time to check.

*Yes, we think there is a reason*
*to be running neck-and-neck*
*and it must be quite important*
*but we don't have time to check.*

Yes, we think there is a reason
to be running neck-and-neck
and it must be quite important...
And if not...well, what the heck.

# Those Dinosaur Blues

I'm a dino
with a low, low voice.
It's not my fault.
I had no choice.
Everyone's afraid of me.
I'm very nice.
Why don't they see?

I've got those di-no-saur blues_____ from my hat to my shoes._____

I'm so ter-ri-bly blue._____ Oh, woe, what can I do? I've got those di-no-saur_____ blues.

I've got those di-no-saur blues. Got no hat. Don't have shoes. But I know if I had,

I would still feel so bad._____ Oh, those di-no-saur_____ blues.

Oh why, oh why
am I the scariest guy?
I am longing to play,
but you all run away
without saying goodbye.
And I just want to cry.
I've got those dinosaur blues.
How I wish I could choose
that you would love me a lot

since I'm cute. But I'm not.
I've got those dinosaur blues.
*Now, no one expects*
*a Tyrannosaurus Rex*
*to be friendly,*
*and silly,*
*and shy.*
*But if you knew me,*
*you'd find*

*that I'm gentle and kind.*
*Yes, I'm really*
*a sensitive guy.*
Oh why, oh why
am I the scariest guy?
I am longing to play,
but you all run away
without saying goodbye.
And I just want to cry.

I've got those dinosaur blues
from my hat to my shoes.
I'm so terribly blue.
Oh, woe, what can I do?
I've got those dinosaur blues.
Boo-hoo, those dinosaur blues.
I'm a dinosaur who's
got those
dinosaur blues.

# Dinosaur, Dinosaur / Jump Rope Jive

SPENCER: Um, excuse me.
MAREN: We have a jump rope song for you.
DINOSAUR: For ME?
MAREN: Yup!
KIDS: *DINOSAUR, DINOSAUR, LONELY AND SHY.*
*DINOSAUR, DINOSAUR, READY TO CRY.*
*TYRANNOSAUR, BANANASAUR, O, SAURUS OF MINE,*
*YOU'VE GOT A LOT OF BUDDIES*
*AND YOU'RE GONNA BE FINE—YOU'VE GOT 1, 2, 3, 4...*
DINOSAUR: Get over that rope and count some more.
KIDS: Yeah!

(SUDDENLY, FROM OUT OF NOWHERE, APPEAR...)
   THE AMAZING SINGING CHICKENS:

Di - no - saur, Di - no - saur, so   lone - ly   and   shy!___   Di - no - saur, Di - no - saur,

read - y   to   cry.___   Ty - ran - no - saur, Ba - na - na - saur, O,   saur - us   of   mine!___   You've

got   a   lot   of   bud - dies   and   you're   gon - na   be   fine.___   gon - na   be   fine.___

You've got **1** and **2** and **3** and **4**.
Get over that rope and
count some more.
You've got to skip in time.
You've got to move your feet.
You've got to keep on counting
to that jump rope beat.
Dinosaur, Dinosaur,
so lonely and shy.   *(Yeah.)*

Dinosaur, Dinosaur,
ready to cry.   *(Oh.)*
Tyrannosaur, Bananasaur,
O, saurus of mine!
You've got a lot of buddies
and you're gonna be fine.
   You've got **5** [CLAP]
   **6** [CLAP] **7** and **8**.
   So many friends,

you can't keep them all straight.
You've got [CLAP, CLAP] **9**,
and [CLAP, CLAP] **10**.
Whenever you miss,
you start it over.
We're gonna start it over again!
Great big Dinosaur,
so lonely and shy.
Dinosaur, Dinosaur,

ready to cry.
Tyrannosaur, Bananasaur,
O, saurus of mine!
You've got a lot of buddies
and you've got a lot of buddies
and you've got a lot of buddies
and you've got a lot of buddies!
And you're gonna be fine!
   *So fine!*

# Pig Island

There is one per-fect place— in the whole wide world Where nos-es are crink - led and tails are curled,— Where squeals are hap - py and smiles are bright,— And the wind is gen - tle all day and night:

*Chorus*

Pig Is - land! Pig Is - land! What a beau-ti - ful place— to be. They play on the beach - es the col - or of peach - es There by the tur - quoise sea, oh, my,— Un - der a blue, blue— sky.

All over Pig Island
there are piggies galore—
I know that there must be
a million or more.
They sing piggy songs
as loud as they please
and wiggle to sleep
in the coconut trees.
(CHORUS)

The only way to get there
is by Piggy Express—
You've got to close your eyes,
and then whisper, *"OOO, YES!"*
A tiny little piggy
with silver wings
touches your hand
and softly sings:
(CHORUS)

And when you arrive,
they're so glad that you came:
They jump up and down
as they call out your name.
Look at them dancing
all along the shore.
You all know the song,
so let's sing it once more:
(CHORUS)

Pig Island! Pig Island!
What a beautiful place to be.
They play on the beaches
the color of peaches
there by the turquoise sea,
oh my,
under a blue, blue sky.
Under a blue, blue sky.
Under...a very blue sky.

SONG #
18

# Pajama Time

The moon is up. It's get-ting late. Let's get read-y to cel - e - brate. It's Pa-

ja - ma Time!— Oh,———— it's Pa - ja - ma Time!—

Pull on the bot-toms, put on the top. Get your-self set to pa - ja-ma-dee-bop. It's Pa-

ja - ma Time!— Yeah,———— it's Pa - ja - ma Time!—

Some are old and some are new.
Some are red and some are blue.
Some are fuzzy. Some are not.
But we can all pajammy
in whatever we've got.
It's Pajama Time!
Yeah, it's Pajama Time!
 Pajammy to the left.
 Pajammy to the right.
 (PAJAMA-JAMA-JAMA-JAMA...P! J's!)
Everybody's wearing them
on Saturday night.
 (PAJAMA-JAMA-JAMA-JAMA...P! J's!)

Now all around the room
in one big line,
wearing our pajamas
and looking so fine.
 *Hup! Un-hunh hunh.*
*Ooooooo!*
Some are pink
and some are green.
Some are the ugliest
you've ever seen.
They might be stripey
or polka dot,
but we can all pajammy

in whatever we've got.
It's Pajama Time!
Yeah, it's Pajama Time!
At the end of the day,
it's got to be Pajama Time.
Now, did you hear what I say?
It's got to be Pajama Time!
 Now hop into bed.
 Turn out the light.
 Get cozy in your covers
 and you say good night.
 Close your little eyes
 and begin to snore...

*But hold on a minute—*
*there's one thing more:*
*Before you go on off to sleep,*
*I just want to say,*
 Turn the light back on
 and look everywhere—
 You've got to find pajamas
 for your **TEDDY BEAR!**
It's Pajama Time!
Whoa-oh, it's Pajama Time!
It's Pajama Time! *Hup!*
It's Pajama Time!
*(Shhhhhhhhh!)*

# Silly Lullaby

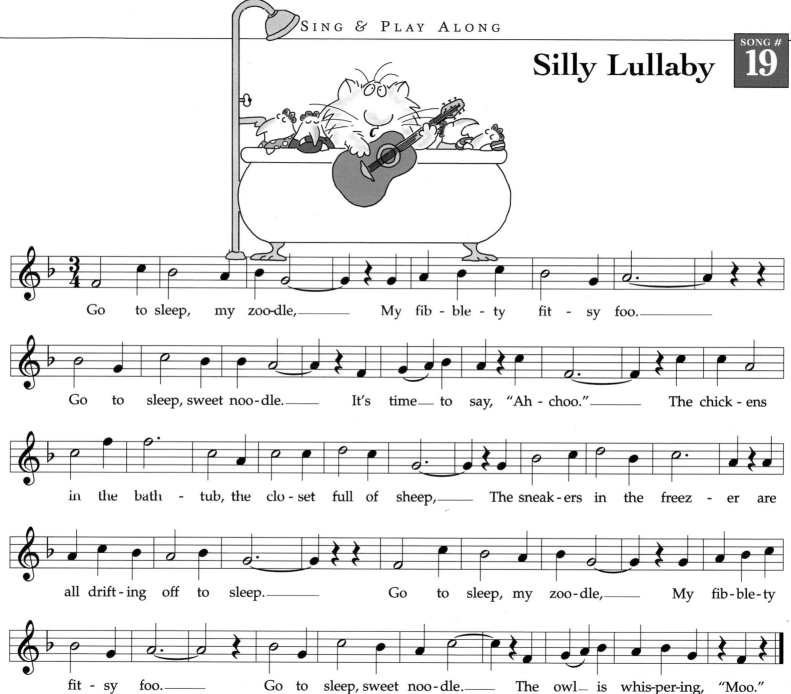

Go to sleep, my zoo-dle,_____ My fib-ble-ty fit-sy foo._____

Go to sleep, sweet noo-dle._____ It's time— to say, "Ah-choo."_____ The chick-ens

in the bath-tub, the clo-set full of sheep,_____ The sneak-ers in the freez-er are

all drift-ing off to sleep._____ Go to sleep, my zoo-dle,_____ My fib-ble-ty

fit-sy foo._____ Go to sleep, sweet noo-dle._____ The owl— is whis-per-ing, "Moo."

# Book Credits
## & Thank-yous

My sincerest and most grateful recognition for the good work, now and always, of the exuberant, fine-feathered people at Workman, my faithful publisher and friends for over twenty years—

EDITOR SUPREME Suzanne Rafer

EXQUISITE DESIGN Paul Hanson

VIGILANT PRODUCTION Elizabeth Gaynor

ATTENTIVE MANAGEMENT OF ART
AND OF TEMPERAMENTAL ARTIST Harry Schroder

UNFLAPPABLE DESIGN FACILITATOR Elizabeth Johnsboen

RELUCTANT VISIONARY Peter Workman

INTERNATIONAL & DOMESTIC DIPLOMACY Carolan Workman

EXCELLENCE & CLASS IN ALL THINGS
Barbie Altorfer, Anne Cherry, Beth Doty, Jim Eber, Rick Grossman,
Philip Hoffhines, Wayne Kirn, Anthony Pedone, Max Sentry, Aurelio Tavarez

Thank you, too, to Ron Ricketts, Christine Antonsen, Kendra Henderson, Wayne Booth, and Andrew Bent at iPLATFORM/Rammgraph, for their careful attention to the many subtleties of art reproduction.

# Recording Credits
## & Thank-yous

are printed sideways and impossibly small

on both sides of this page———————▶

SO, if you find that your CD wants to

go along with you someplace, but

your book prefers to hang around home, you could

make a lovely and informative holder for the CD.

Simply cut where indicated, fold the 2 side flaps inward,

then insert this *plus* your

PHILADELPHIA CHICKENS CD

into a new, clear plastic case

(available at lots of stores).

Or maybe just use the case of a CD that

you don't really like all that much anymore.

FOLD ——▶

FOLD ——▶

CUT HERE
VERTICALLY

"Those Chickens of Swing"

# Philadelphia Chickens

*and* 17½ OTHER HIGHLY UNLIKELY SONGS by BOYNTON and FORD *with* LYRICS BY SANDRA BOYNTON

PERFORMED BY 24 TERRIFIC ACTORS *who can sing!*

1. **Cows** [2:48]
THE SELDOM HERD
KYLA BOYNTON, MICHAEL FORD,
DEVIN MCEWAN & JAMIE MCEWAN
Recorded at THE BARN • SALISBURY, CT
Engineer MICHAEL FORD

2. **Nobody Understands Me** [2:31]
MERYL STREEP
*with* JANE IRA BLOOM, ALTO SAXOPHONE
Recorded at TRIPLE Z STUDIO • NYC Engineer PAUL GUZZONE
and at THE HIT FACTORY • NYC Engineer CHRIS TERGESEN

3. **Philadelphia Chickens** [3:20]
THE BACON BROTHERS
Recorded at THE HIT FACTORY • NYC
Engineer CHRIS TERGESEN

4. **Be Like a Duck** [2:59]
KEITH BOYNTON
Recorded at THE BARN • SALISBURY, CT
Engineer MICHAEL FORD

5. **Please, Can I Keep It?** [2:25]
LAURA LINNEY
Recorded at THE LAKE HOUSE • TACONIC, CT
Engineer MICHAEL FORD

6. **Snuggle Puppy** [1:44]
ERIC STOLTZ
*with* BETH ANDRIEN
Recorded at TRIPLE Z STUDIO • NYC
Engineer PAUL GUZZONE

7. **I Like to Fuss** [2:38]
PATTI LUPONE
Recorded at THE HOTCHKISS SCHOOL • LAKEVILLE, CT
Engineer FABIO WITKOWSKI

8. **Snoozers** [2:34]
THE BACON BROTHERS
MICHAEL BACON, ACOUSTIC GUITAR
Recorded at TRIPLE Z STUDIO • NYC
Engineer PAUL GUZZONE

9. **Faraway Cookies** [3:31]
CAITLIN MCEWAN
Recorded at THE BARN • SALISBURY, CT
Engineer MICHAEL FORD

10. **The Intermission Song!** [2:12]
AAAARDVARKS
MARK LINN-BAKER, JOE GRIFASI,
MICHAEL GROSS, & DEVIN MCEWAN

Recorded at THE HIT FACTORY • NYC
Engineer CHRIS TERGESEN

11. **Fifteen Animals** [1:54]
JOHN STEY
*with* ADAM BRYANT, WHISTLING
& PAM BOYNTON, WHISTLE
Recorded at TRIPLE Z STUDIO • NYC
Engineer PAUL GUZZONE

12. **Belly Button (Round)** [2:22]
THE HEATH SISTERS
Recorded at THE BARN • SALISBURY, CT
Engineer MICHAEL FORD

13. **BusyBusyBusy** [1:59]
KEVIN KLINE
Recorded at TRIPLE Z STUDIO • NYC
Engineer PAUL GUZZONE

14. **Those Dinosaur Blues** [3:06]
MICHAEL FORD
Recorded at DAISY LANE STUDIO • MALVERN, PA
Engineer MICHAEL FORD

15. **Dinosaur, Dinosaur** [0:26]
DARCY BOYNTON
*with* SPENCER SHERRILL & MAREN WILSON
Recorded at THE BARN • SALISBURY, CT
Engineer MICHAEL FORD

16. **Jump Rope Jive** [1:24]
BETH ANDRIEN
*with* HER HIGHER SELF, & HER ALTO EGO
Recorded at DAISY LANE STUDIO • MALVERN, PA
Engineer MICHAEL FORD

17. **Pig Island** [2:46]
SCOTT BAKULA
Recorded at TRIPLE Z STUDIO • NYC
Engineer PAUL GUZZONE

18. **Pajama Time** [2:18]
ADAM BRYANT
Recorded at TRIPLE Z STUDIO • NYC
Engineer PAUL GUZZONE

19. **Silly Lullaby** [1:20]
NATASHA RICHARDSON
Recorded at TRIPLE Z STUDIO • NYC
Engineer PAUL GUZZONE

20. **Philadelphia Chickens** [3:10]
*instrumental reprise*
TOTAL PROGRAM 48:12

Thank you.

## THANK YOU

QUINTESSENTIALLY TO

**JAMIE McEWAN** (with great love from Sandy)
**BETH ANDRIEN** (with great love from Mike)

**Kathleen Sherrill**
FOR BAILING OUT THE WATER A LOT FASTER
THAN THE SHIP CAN SINK

**Caitlin McEwan**
FOR PERFECT HELP IN EVERY WAY

**Keith Boynton**
FOR ENVIABLE COOL, AND WARMTH

**Devin McEwan**
FOR THE AARDVARKIAN CONCEPT

**Darcy Boynton**
FOR POOKIFUL CONTRIBUTIONS*

AND A NOD TO STEPHEN LUNDEEN,
FOR A TRULY INSPIRING LOVE OF CHICKENS

AND, FOR ENCOURAGEMENT & STEADFAST FRIENDSHIP

Jeanne Boynton, Jood & Rick
Pam & John, Laurie & Carl
Laura Linney, Sarah Getz
Brian Mann & Renée Katz
Salvatore & Lisa Biagini
Jane & Mark Capcelatro
Jenifer & Mark Clarke
Jacquelyn Tintle, Linda Epstein
Robin Corey, Susan Spano
Bevan & Alinda Stanley
Nora & Bob Rivkin
Bill & Sue Kirber
Randy Dwenger, Steve Callahan
Sam & Ellen Posey
Christine Stevens, Stephen Zero

*NAMELY, insisting that *Dinosaur Blues* needed resolution; for two great lines—
"Did we mention we're cows?" and "Technically, we're not cows..."—and
for cheerfully taking care of Dad

Boynton! recordings

---

Most backup vocals by Michael Ford
Three truly peculiar cameos by Sandra Boynton

Except as noted above, all instruments played by
MICHAEL FORD

All songs mixed by
CHRIS TERGESEN
at The Hit Factory, Sound on Sound, & Avatar • NYC
Assistant engineers: KATHRYN DIEHL, MICHAEL McCOY,
BART MIGAL, CLAUDIUS MITTENDORFER,
BRIAN MONTGOMERY, PAT WOODWARD

Album mastered by
CHRIS GEHRINGER
at Sterling Sound, NYC
Assistant engineer: WILL QUINNELL

PRODUCED BY SANDRA BOYNTON

All Lyrics by SANDRA BOYNTON
All Arrangements by MICHAEL FORD
with SANDRA BOYNTON

Music by—
*Cows* BOYNTON
*Nobody Understands Me* FORD
*Philadelphia Chickens* BOYNTON
*Be Like a Duck* BOYNTON
*Please, Can I Keep It?* FORD
*Snuggle Puppy* FORD
*I Like to Fuss* FORD
*Snoozers* BOYNTON/FORD
*Faraway Cookies* BOYNTON/FORD
*The Intermission Song* BOYNTON/FORD
*Fifteen Animals* BOYNTON/FORD
*Belly Button (Round)* BOYNTON
*BusyBusyBusy* FORD
*Those Dinosaur Blues* BOYNTON
*Jump Rope Jive* FORD
*Pig Island* BOYNTON/FORD
*Pajama Time* FORD
*Silly Lullaby* BOYNTON

The Bacon Brothers appear courtesy of Rounder Records
The Heath Sisters appear courtesy of Acoustic Nightingale Records
Patti LaPone appears courtesy of LaVZlay Records

---

FOR CHEERFUL AND EFFICIENT LOGISTICAL HELP
Jerry Kovarski at Korg
Jennifer Almquist at The Hotchkiss School
Betsy Bacon at Forosoco Music
Mary Ellen Bernard at Triple Z
David Lollar at ICM
Zoe Thrall at The Hit Factory
Sara Arlotti at Sound on Sound
Andreanna Candi at Sterling Sound
Jon Adler
Amy Bradley
Joanna Cannon
William Derella, Susan Mieras
Pam Lister, Krista LaFrenz
Emily Sklar
Joanne Sohrweide
The St. Regis Hotel, NYC
The Adam's Mark Hotel, Philadelphia

FOR JUMP ROPE DEVELOPMENT
Elise Sophia Babigian, Lily Beler, Jacqueline George, Devin Hardy,
Caroline Johanson, Kelley Merwin, Christian Sherrill, Lauren Stellato, April Tierney

FOR GOOD WORK
F. M. Alexander, David Allender, Fred Astaire

*Pajama Time* is based on Sandra Boynton's board book published by Workman Publishing
*Snoozers* is based on Sandra Boynton's board book published by Simon & Schuster

Cover Design: Paul Hanson & Sandra Boynton
Layout: Sandra Boynton

© and ℗2002 Sandra Boynton. ALL RIGHTS RESERVED
*Cows, Philadelphia Chickens, Be Like a Duck, Belly Button (Round),
Those Dinosaur Blues, Silly Lullaby* © S K Boynton Music (ASCAP)
All other songs © Boynton/Ford Music (ASCAP)

Please visit our web site, such as it is: WWW.BOYNTONSONGS.COM
ALL RIGHTS OF THE PRODUCER AND OWNERS OF THE WORK REPRODUCED
ON THE CD ARE RESERVED. UNAUTHORIZED COPYING, HIRING, LENDING,
PUBLIC PERFORMANCE, AND BROADCASTING ARE PROHIBITED.

Published, and sold as a book/CD set, by
WORKMAN PUBLISHING COMPANY, INC. • NEW YORK, N.Y.